# ALIENS™

publisher **Mike Richardson**

series editor **Barbara Kesel**
collection editor **Suzanne Taylor**
collection designer **Teena Gores**
book design manager **Brian Gogolin**

special thanks to **Cindy Irwin at Twentieth Century Fox +
Steve Perry + Den Beauvais + Monty Sheldon** and **Jamie S. Rich**

inspired by **The original Alien designs of H.R. Giger**

**ALIENS™: GENOCIDE**
Published by Titan Books Ltd. by arrangement with Dark
Horse Comics, Inc. Aliens™ and © 1986, 1997 Twentieth
Century Fox Film Corporation. Aliens™ is a trademark of
Twentieth Century Fox Film Corporation. All rights reserved.
Text and illustrations © 1992, 1997 Twentieth Century Fox
Film Corporation. All other material, unless otherwise
specified, © 1997 Dark Horse Comics, Inc. All rights reserved.
The stories, institutions, and characters in this collection
are fictional. Any resemblance to actual persons, living or
dead, without satiric intent, is purely coincidental. No portion
of this publication may be reproduced, by any means, without
the express permission of Twentieth Century Fox Film
Corporation and Dark Horse Comics, Inc. Dark Horse Comics®
and the Dark Horse logo are registered trademarks of Dark
Horse Comics, Inc.

This book collects issues one through four of the Dark Horse
comic-book series **Aliens™**: Genocide.

Published by
Titan Books Ltd.
42-44 Dolben Street
London SE1 0UP

First edition: April 1997
ISBN: 1-85286-805-8

| 1 | 2 | 3 | 4 | 5 | 6 | 7 | 8 | 9 | 10 |

Printed in Canada

# ALIENS™
## GENOCIDE

story **Mike Richardson**

script **John Arcudi**

pencils **Damon Willis**

inks **Karl Story**

colors **Arthur Suydam**

cover **John Bolton**

lettering **Jim Massara**

**TITAN BOOKS**

*Genocide.*

Maybe you saw the moody John Bolton cover and decided to check it out. Maybe you remembered the powerful Dave Dorman painting from the first edition. Maybe you remembered back farther to the lush Arthur Suydam paintings from the comics issues of *Aliens: Genocide*. Maybe that word was just intriguing in itself: genocide. Species death. So what's going on here?

It started with the movies. *Alien*, *Aliens*, and *Alien³* created the starting point for a series of Dark Horse comics that expanded the underlying mythos begun in those movies to the point where more story now exists in four-color form than in film-stock form. This story is just a small dip of the toe into the fetid waters of Aliens lore; check out the list at the back of the book for the rest of the ongoing Aliens saga.

First there were Aliens. Aliens versus humans. Then, Aliens versus Predators. So, one day, the thought rang through the halls: what about Aliens versus Aliens? Now there's an event!

Mark Verheiden, scripter of the first three volumes of Dark Horse's Aliens tales, was busy at work on Predator, so we needed a new guy. Somebody who knew how to spin a yarn made of equal parts acid and glory; somebody with a twisted sensibility capable of monstrous mayhem and spellbinding storytelling; somebody like John Arcudi.

Arcudi is one of the *cleanest* writers in the business. Not in the sense of "this one's for children," but the kind of lucid, flawlessly paced scene-setting that gets across a universe of ideas with every carefully chosen phrase and efficiently paced scene. There's no unnecessary purple prose here; just the characters, ma'am, and no extra words to bring attention to the writer's extensive collection of "learn-a-word-a-day" calendars. Wish I had that talent.

Arcudi's also a delightfully scary-looking guy. When those soul-killer eyes make contact, they inspire thoughts of dark alleys and mysterious mayhem, dread deeds and terrifying tales (did I mention that he doesn't dabble in endless alliteration or meaningless metaphor or pointless pontification like some wordy writers?), making him the perfect image of the horror-story writer. Joke is that he's really extremely personable and outrageously well read. Anybody who reads Benchley (Robert, that is) and knows that the Algonquin Roundtable didn't include King Arthur is tops in my book.

So, John put together a planetary civil war, then threw some humans into the mix to make it a really creepy place to visit, even on an imaginary basis. So, great! Now that we had a story, we needed somebody who wanted to draw Aliens. Lots of Aliens. And Alien parts . . . enter the artist.

Damon Willis didn't have a lot of professional credits under his belt when his samples got him the *Genocide* job, and he clearly had no idea what he was getting himself into. Heh-heh-heh. He said he wanted to draw Aliens; we said, "Okay, here are some Aliens. Oh, and give us two separate species (note the subtle differences between the two queens . . .) and about five million of each type, okay? When I saw the original art for the first page of issue three, I laughed out loud and asked Damon where to look to find Waldo. The boy does not skimp on the detail.

Next step was making sure none of those Aliens lost any detail. Karl Story's a detail man. Think of him as the "hand polish" of inkers; the pages always come back sparkling. An inker obliterates the original pencils in the process of changing them to ink lines; Karl's one of the few names that makes pencillers sigh in contentment — they know he won't do 'em wrong.

The wash of colorist Arthur Suydam's watercolors mimics the acidic sheen of the Aliens, giving *Genocide* that great "ooky" feel. While color-separation technology has improved dramatically since the system used to produce the film for this book, it's still possible to appreciate the textures and washes that were impossible to produce mechanically at the time. (Sounds like I'm talking decades ago, right? As computers go, it's been geological eras!)

So, take a look inside. It's dark and creepy, and there are monsters everywhere. Blame John Arcudi — I always do. Not that he deserves anything but praise as does the rest of *Genocide*'s creative crew. Uh . . . is that enough, guys? Wanna let me out now? I can't see in here . . . uh, guys? Guys? What was that noi —

Barbara Kesel
Portland, OR
1996

Suydam's *Aliens: Genocide* #4 cover art

# ALIENS™

IT IS THE BIRTHPLACE OF DEMONS.

YET HERE, THERE ARE NO RAGING FIRES, NO STENCH OF BRIMSTONE, NO RIVERS OF BLOOD OR WAILING OF TORTURED SOULS.

THE MATRIARCH OF HELL HAS BEEN DEPOSED, AND HER SUBJECTS ARE IN DISARRAY, UNABLE TO FUNCTION.

THEY ARE AIMLESS, SILENT.

ONLY THE ROYAL GUARD MOVES QUICKLY TO ESTABLISH THE NEW SOVEREIGN.

BUT THE PRIMORDIAL PALACE HAS BEEN VIOLATED; IT HAS BEEN DEEMED UNSAFE AND UNCLEAN.

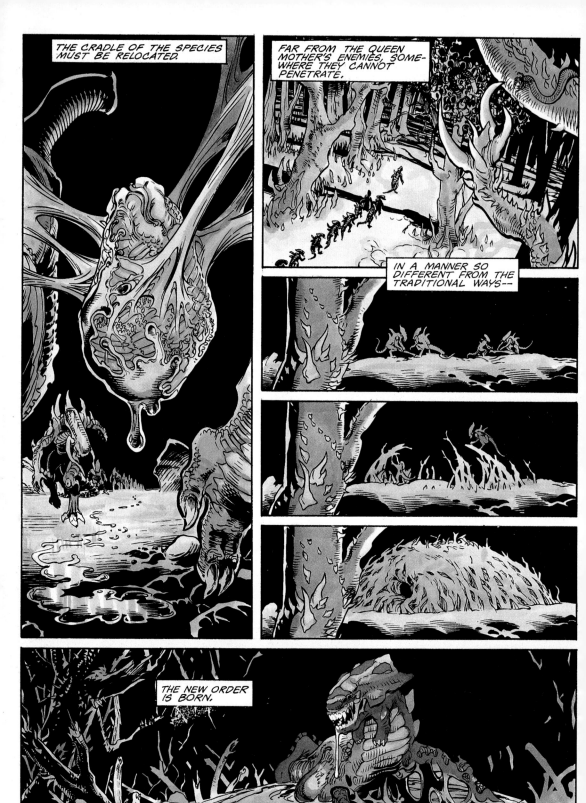

HOWEVER, THE UNPRECEDENTED LOSS OF THE EMPIRE'S GENETRIX HAS LEFT THE CITIZENS WITHOUT ANY LINK, UNABLE TO COMMUNICATE.

SLOWLY, THEY ACT, OUT OF A NEED TO FILL THE VOID.

AND FILL IT THEY DO.

THE OLD ORDER IS FAR FROM GONE.

THE MISTRESS OF ONE KINGDOM CALLS OUT TO HER NATION.

THE MISTRESS OF ANOTHER SENDS OUT HER OWN COMMAND.

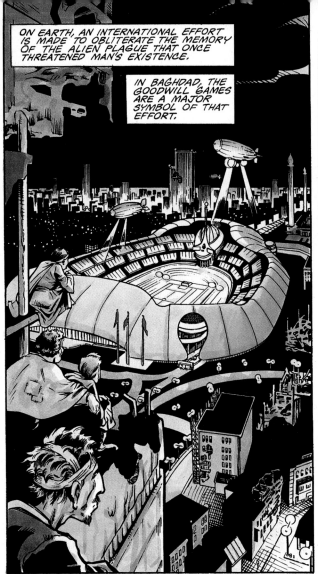

ON EARTH, AN INTERNATIONAL EFFORT IS MADE TO OBLITERATE THE MEMORY OF THE ALIEN PLAGUE THAT ONCE THREATENED MAN'S EXISTENCE.

IN BAGHDAD, THE GOODWILL GAMES ARE A MAJOR SYMBOL OF THAT EFFORT.

WAR IS NO MORE THAN AN UNWELCOME PHANTOM HERE.

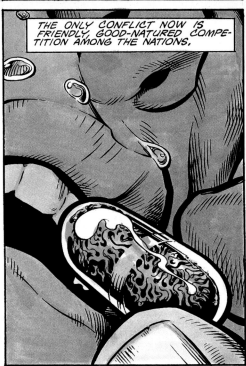

THE ONLY CONFLICT NOW IS FRIENDLY, GOOD-NATURED COMPETITION AMONG THE NATIONS.

A SPIRIT OF FAIR PLAY AND CAMARADERIE SUFFUSES THE PARTICIPANTS.

HEY, TIME TO LINE UP.

SLAP

HUH? OH, YEAH, OKAY.

SNAP

BANG!

AND WE CAN'T BE CAUGHT WITH OUR PANTS DOWN IF WE SHOULD EXPERIENCE ANOTHER SUCH INVASION.

BUT PUBLIC SENTIMENT IS "ANTI-WAR-MACHINE" RIGHT NOW. THEY JUST DON'T WANT TO THINK ABOUT IT.

SO, IF WE CAN'T GET GOVERNMENT FUNDING FOR NEW AND IMPROVED EQUIPMENT, WE DO THE NEXT BEST THING.

WE MAKE A NEW AND IMPROVED *SOLDIER* FOR JUST A FEW BUCKS A HEAD.

JUST WHAT THE HELL ARE YOU TALKING ABOUT, LEON?!

*THAT.* THAT IS WHAT I'M TALKING ABOUT.

NOW WATCH THIS.

HUHN!

OOOF!

YAAAH!

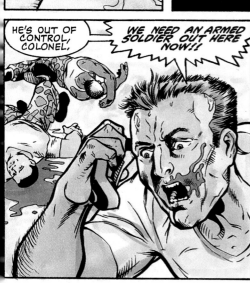

HE'S OUT OF CONTROL, COLONEL!

WE NEED AN ARMED SOLDIER OUT HERE NOW!!

COLONAAAAAAIII!!!!

DAMMIT, JOHN, JUST FLICK IT TO THE LEFT!

I'M TELLING YOU, IT'S STUCK!

JEEZ-US, JOHN, WATCH OUT!

BUDDABUDDA

KRAK

YAAAEEEE!

BUDDAB!

BOB, I'VE BEEN GETTING REPORTS THAT OUR XENO-ZIP IS NOT QUITE SO MARVELOUS AS WE FIRST THOUGHT.

IN FACT, IT SEEMS THAT A NUMBER OF OUR CUSTOMERS GET A BIT,...UH, CARRIED AWAY.

WHAT CAN YOU TELL ME ABOUT THIS?

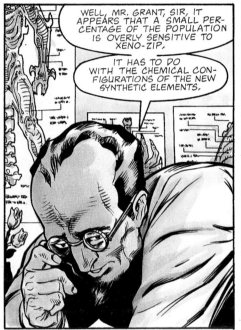

WELL, MR. GRANT, SIR, IT APPEARS THAT A SMALL PERCENTAGE OF THE POPULATION IS OVERLY SENSITIVE TO XENO-ZIP.

IT HAS TO DO WITH THE CHEMICAL CONFIGURATIONS OF THE NEW SYNTHETIC ELEMENTS.

C'MON, BOB, HOW ABOUT THAT IN ENGLISH, EH?

WELL, SIR, IT APPEARS THAT OUR FORMULA FOR XENO-ZIP IS IMPERFECT.

THERE WERE CERTAIN ELEMENTS IN THE ORIGINAL FORMULA WHICH CAN'T BE FOUND HERE ON EARTH.

WE THOUGHT WE HAD SUITABLY MIMICKED THESE ELEMENTS, BUT THE FACT IS, WE DIDN'T.

WE CAN'T.

AHH, RIGHT, YOU'RE TALKING ABOUT THAT ALIEN GOO, WHAT WAS IT CALLED, REGAL JAM?

ROYAL JELLY, SIR.

THE ROYAL JELLY WAS TRANSPORTED TO EARTH WITH THE QUEEN MOTHER WHE--

YOU'RE SAYING THAT THESE PEOPLE, THIS SMALL GROUP OF PEOPLE, ARE REACTING TO THE *FAKE* ELEMENTS IN XENO-ZIP?

WELL, THAT'S ONE WAY OF PUTTING IT, THOUGH I'D--

BUT IF WE HAD THE *REAL* THING, THIS ROYAL JELLY, THEN WE'D HAVE A PERFECT PRODUCT, CORRECT?

ER, UH, YES, WE THINK SO.

BUT THERE IS ONLY ONE KNOWN SOURCE OF THE JELLY, SIR.

WELL THEN, WE'RE JUST GOING TO HAVE TO GO THERE AND GET IT, AREN'T WE?

GENTLEMEN, WE'VE ALL GOT WORK TO DO, SO HOP TO IT.

OF COURSE, MR. GRANT.

YESSIR,

RIGHT AWAY, SIR.

ABSOLUTELY, SIR,

ANYTHING YOU SAY, MR. GRANT --*SIR.*

NORTH CAROLINA IS "FRIENDLY" TERRAIN, BUT THOSE BUGS HAVE THE RUN OF THEIR PLANET, CORRECT?

YES, GENERAL, BUT MY RESEARCHERS ASSURE ME THAT THE HOMEWORLD STRAIN IS A LESS AGGRESSIVE BREED.

IN THEIR OWN NATURAL ENVIRONMENT, WHERE THEY EVOLVED, THERE IS A DELICATELY BALANCED ECOSYSTEM.

THEY HAVE PREDATORS THERE TO KEEP THEM IN CHECK.

REMOVING THEM FROM THAT WORLD, ELIMINATING THE PREDATORS, HAS TURNED THEM INTO WHAT THEY ARE TODAY.

THAT ALL SOUNDS VERY GOOD, BUT LET'S NOT FORGET THE QUEEN MOTHER CAME FROM HOMEWORLD.

I'VE ONLY HEARD THE STORIES, BUT THEY'RE ENOUGH TO MAKE ME RATHER WARY OF THIS SORT OF MISSION.

WELL, JUST LIKE ANY OTHER FEMALE, I'M SURE SHE CAN BE A PERFECT BITCH--

BUT THE BEAUTY OF IT IS, WE CAN JUST *SHOOT* HER.

NOW LET'S CUT OUT THE CRAP, AND GET DOWN TO BUSINESS.

GRANT, WHY THE HELL SHOULD WE HELP YOU? FACT IS, WE KINDA LIKE THIS XENO-ZIP STUFF THE WAY IT IS.

WELL, YOU'RE ALONE THERE, SIR, BERSERKERS ARE NOT MUCH USE IN THE PRIVATE SECTOR.

LAWSUITS WILL FORCE ME TO STOP MAKING XENO-ZIP ALTOGETHER, SOMETHING YOU'D RATHER NOT SEE, CORRECT?

BUT I MIGHT BE PERSUADED TO FEND OFF ALL LAWSUITS AND CONTINUE PRODUCTION.

PERHAPS AN AGREEMENT COULD BE DRAWN UP, ASSURING THE ARMED FORCES OF AN UNINTERRUPTED SUPPLY OF THE "FLAWED" XENO-ZIP.

UNLESS, OF COURSE, OFFICER SHRINKING VIOLET DISAPPROVES.

WELL, BURTON-- WHAT DO YOU THINK?

NILES, I'M ONLY PRESIDING HERE. THIS IS YOUR SHOW.

I'M WILLING TO GIVE YOU THE OKAY ON A STAFFED DEEP-SPACE TACTICAL VESSEL.

WELL, GRANT, IT LOOKS LIKE WE CAN WORK SOMETHING OUT.

GLAD TO HEAR IT, GENERAL, GLAD TO HEAR IT.

LEAVE THE EGGHEAD WORK TO ME AND MY STAFF. YOU JUST PROVIDE THE GUNS, THE GRUNTS AND THE GONDOLA.

YOU WILL, OF COURSE, GIVE ME THE BEST MEN FOR THE JOB.

YOUR COMMANDING OFFICER WILL BE MAJOR ALEX LEE, A KEY PLAYER IN THE ALIEN MOP-UP, AND THE YOUNGEST HOLDER OF THE CONGRESSIONAL MEDAL OF HONOR.

WELL, WELL, SOUNDS LIKE I'LL BE IN GOOD HANDS.

CAN'T WAIT TO MEET THE MAN.

HARD TO BELIEVE THAT THE ARMY PUT THIS ALL TOGETHER FOR ME IN JUST UNDER A MONTH, EH, WYCKOFF?

MR. GRANT, SIR, ARE YOU SURE YOUR PRESENCE ON THIS MISSION IS REQUIRED?

NOT ONLY IS IT DANGEROUS, BUT A LOT COULD HAPPEN WHILE YOU'RE GONE.

WYCKOFF, THIS MISSION IS *EVERYTHING!* NEO-PHARM IS DOOMED IF THIS MISSION FAILS.

WHATEVER ELSE HAPPENS IS SECONDARY, UNDERSTAND?

AH, MY TECHNICAL STAFF OF RESEARCHERS AND ADVISERS.

I'M SURE THEY'LL KEEP ME OUT OF TROUBLE.

"ONLY, WHO THE HELL IS THAT GUY?"

"THAT'S BEGALLI, SIR. HE JUMPED SHIP FROM MEDTECH A FEW MONTHS BACK, BUT HIS ALIEN KNOWLEDGE IS UNSURPASSED. I'M SURE HE'LL BE OF GREAT ASSISTANCE."

I'LL HAVE TO TAKE YOUR-- *GOOD LORD*, WYCKOFF, WOULD YOU LOOK AT THAT!

NOW *THAT'S A MAN!*

THAT'S *MAJOR* LEE.

AND YEAH, YOU'RE A CIVILIAN, BUT YOU'RE ALSO THE ONE WHO WANTED TO PLAY "BIG WHITE HUNTER," SO GET USED TO THE ATMOSPHERE.

DO YOU SUPPOSE WE COULD DISCUSS THIS *AFTER* I GET DRESSED--

MAJOR LEE?

GOD! WHAT A WAY TO WAKE UP!

HEY, IT'S THAT BIG FELLA! CORPORAL, CORPORAL-- DAMN, WHAT'S HIS NAME AGAIN?

HENRIKSEN! HOW ARE YOU?

FINE, SIR.

ZZIP

CPL HENRIKSEN

SAY, THAT MAJOR OF YOURS IS A REAL PAIN IN THE ASS, EH?

SHE'S TOUGH, BUT I THINK THAT'S GOOD.

THE MATERIAL WE WANT IS IN THE LARGE, CENTRAL SACK.

BUT *THESE* SMALLER PODS ARE WHAT WE MUST KEEP OUR EYES ON.

IN FACT, ANY ONE OF THOSE SMALLER PODS MAY CONTAIN AN INCREDIBLY VICIOUS CREATURE--

MORE DANGEROUS THAN ANY YOU OR I HAVE ENCOUNTERED TO DATE.

EXCEPT MY MOTHER-IN-LAW.

ANYWAY, THIS IS ALL SECOND-HAND INFO, AND I CAN'T GUARANTEE ITS ACCURACY.

SO, LET'S MOVE ON TO SOMETHING I KNOW A LITTLE MORE ABOUT.

CLICK

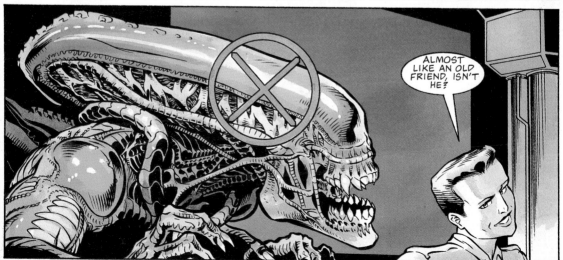

ALMOST LIKE AN OLD FRIEND, ISN'T HE?

I WANT TO TELL YOU WHY YOU SHOULD AVOID THESE TARGETS.

WHILE A SHOT TO THE CHEST WILL CERTAINLY STOP THE CREATURE, IT WILL ALSO CREATE A VERY BLOODY WOUND.

THE SAME CAN BE SAID FOR THE HEAD, AND THE SPATTER POTENTIAL IS EVEN GREATER THERE.

AS MANY OF YOU HAVE ALREADY DISCOVERED, A SHOT TO THE KNEE WILL NOT ONLY HAMPER THE ALIEN'S MOBILITY--

BUT SUCH A WOUND ALSO MINIMIZES BLEEDING AND SPATTER POTENTIAL.

CLICK

I KNOW THE BLOOD ISSUE IS OF GREAT CONCERN TO ALL OF YOU, SO I'M HAPPY TO PRESENT AN INNOVATION WHICH SHOULD ALL BUT DO AWAY WITH YOUR FEARS.

FOR MORE ON THAT, I TURN YOU OVER TO DR. ZATO.

LADIES AND GENTLEMEN, I GIVE YOU YOUR NEXT BEST FRIEND.

THE Z-110 ACID NEUTRALIZING COMBAT WARDROBE.

EFFORTS TO PRODUCE AN ARMOR RESISTANT TO THE INTENSE ACIDITY OF THE ALIEN BLOOD HAVE PROVED IMPRACTICAL.

TOO HEAVY, AND ALL THAT. THEREFORE, WE MUST NOT RESIST, BUT EXTIRPATE.

THE MOMENT ALIEN BLOOD TOUCHES THIS WARDROBE, THE THREAT IS ELIMINATED ALTOGETHER.

IT IS LINED WITH A GELATINOUS SUBSTANCE THAT CAN NEUTRALIZE THE ACID, GIVING IT THE pH BALANCE OF WATER.

THIS IS ALL OLD NEWS TO YOU, MAJOR.

WOULD YOU PLEASE COME WITH ME? I HAVE SOMETHING VERY IMPORTANT TO SHOW YOU.

SORRY ABOUT MY BEHAVIOR EARLIER, MAJOR, I'M USUALLY PRETTY GRUMPY WHEN I FIRST WAKE UP.

ESPECIALLY AFTER 12 WEEKS.

RIGHT.

WHAT I'M ABOUT TO SHOW YOU TWO IS STRICTLY HUSH-HUSH. I DON'T WANT ANY-ONE TO KNOW ABOUT THIS, ESPECIALLY NOT THE OTHER MEN--

OR WOMEN.

WHAT HAPPENED HERE? ISN'T THIS SUPPOSED TO BE A STORAGE CHAMBER?

YES, AND IN A WAY, IT STILL IS, BUT THE CARGO IS WHAT'S DIFFERENT.

GLAD YOU COULD MAKE IT, MR. GRANT.

I BELIEVE IT'S ABOUT TO START.

MR. GRANT, WHY IS THIS SUCH A BIG SECRET?

WELL, CORPORAL, I KNOW MOST MARINES HAVE COME TO REALLY HATE THE ALIENS.

AND THIS JUST MIGHT PISS THEM OFF.

WHAT IS THAT THING?!

WHY, IT'S A DONOR CLONE.

THEY'RE USUALLY PRODUCED FOR THE PURPOSE OF ORGAN AND TISSUE DONATION.

I'LL ADMIT, IT ISN'T THE MOST ATTRACTIVE CREATURE, BUT IT'S PROVED USEFUL.

I'M PROUD TO SAY, ITS CELLS OF ORIGINATION WERE RETRIEVED FROM MY WRIST.

DR. FRIEL, THE CLONE'S VITAL SIGNS HAVE GONE IRREGULAR.

IT'S BEGINNING.

WHAT THE HELL IS GOING ON HERE, GRANT?

WATCH, MAJOR.

JUST WATCH.

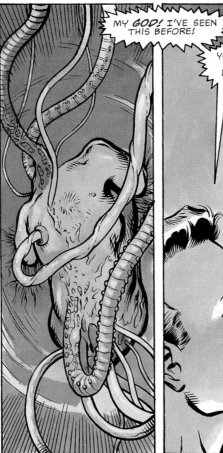

MY *GOD!* I'VE SEEN THIS BEFORE!

YOU'RE BREEDING ONE OF THOSE DAMN THINGS!

TAKE IT EASY, THE HOST ISN'T REALLY ALIVE; IT CAN'T FEEL ANY PAIN.

HERE IT COMES.

SCREEEEEEE

I'VE SEEN ENOUGH! COME ON, CORPORAL!

MAJOR, WAIT, LET ME EXPLAIN.

"YOU'VE GOT THIS ALL WRONG."

WHEN THERE ARE NO CYCLES OF THE SUN AND MOON TO DISTINGUISH THE DAYS, HOW DOES ONE MARK THE PASSING OF TIME?

BREAKFAST, LUNCH AND DINNER.

FOR CHRISSAKES, JASTROW, GIVE IT A REST!!

WHASSA MATTER, ELLIS? I THOUGHT YOU LIKED MUSIC.

I LIKE MUSIC FINE, BUT NOT BLARING IN MY EAR, AND *NOT WHILE I'M EATING!*

JUST A LITTLE ANXIOUS, IS ALL, AND WHO CAN BLAME YOU? I MEAN, WE GOT SOME HEAVY SHIT AHEAD OF US.

SO I'LL LET YOU HAVE A LITTLE OF MY STASH.

XENO ZIP

I GOT PLENTY OF MINE LEFT, AND YOU SHOULD SAVE YOURS.

THEY'RE SUPPOSED TO BE FOR ENDURANCE, REMEMBER? AND I DOUBT WE'LL GET MUCH SLEEP ONCE WE TOUCH DOWN AT "BUG" CENTRAL.

HEY, CHECK IT OUT. HENRIKSEN'S DOING IT AGAIN. HE'S TAKING HIS FOOD TO HIS ROOM.

THEY MAKE MODELS THAT EAT, YOU KNOW.

IT AIN'T JUST THAT, HE WON'T SHOWER WITH US, I NEVER SEEN HIM SHAVE--

AND, FAR AS I CAN TELL, THIS IS HIS FIRST COMBAT MISSION.

JASTROW

U.S.M.C.

A GUY THAT SIZE, ON A PLANET CRAWLING WITH CRICKETS, AND HE NEVER SAW ANY COMBAT?

I'M TELLING YOU, THE BASTARD AIN'T HUMAN.

WHY DON'T YOU JUST SAY WHAT'S ON YOUR MIND, PUNK?!

COME ON, SAY IT TO MY FACE!!

SAY IT!!

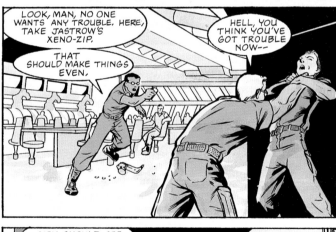

LOOK, MAN, NO ONE WANTS ANY TROUBLE. HERE, TAKE JASTROW'S XENO-ZIP.

THAT SHOULD MAKE THINGS EVEN.

HELL, YOU THINK YOU'VE GOT TROUBLE NOW--

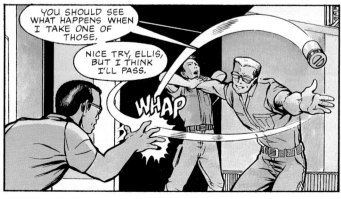

YOU SHOULD SEE WHAT HAPPENS WHEN I TAKE ONE OF THOSE.

NICE TRY, ELLIS, BUT I THINK I'LL PASS.

WHAP

I COULD HAVE HANDLED THAT, MR. GRANT.

YES, I KNOW.

THOSE PEOPLE HAVE TO KNOW, NOT YOU. PRETTY SOON, THEIR LIVES WILL DEPEND ON HOW MUCH THEY RESPECT ME.

MAJOR, THEY ALL RESPECT YOU, AND WITH GOOD REASON.

THERE'S NO WAY MY BREAKING UP A HISSY FIT IS GOING TO UNDERMINE THAT RESPECT.

MAYBE SO, BUT YOU STI--

THIS IS NOT WHAT I WANTED TO TALK ABOUT.

I WANT TO EXPLAIN THE ALIEN INCUBATION.

I DON'T THINK I WANT TO HEAR THIS.

BELIEVE IT OR NOT--

I'M TRYING TO SAVE LIVES.

WHAT?!! WHAT THE HELL ARE YOU TALKING ABOUT?!

YOU'RE RISKING GOOD MARINE LIVES FOR THIS FRIGGING JELLY, FOR PROFIT, YOU RUTHLESS BASTARD!!

AS WELL AS MY OWN LIFE, AND I'LL HAVE TO DO IT AGAIN AS SOON AS I RUN OUT OF THE STUFF, UNLESS I CAN BRING A SOURCE HOME WITH ME.

NO WAY, MISTER! IF YOU WANT TO KIDNAP THAT QUEEN MOTHER THING, YOU'RE NOT USING MY PEOPLE!!

THAT'S NOT WHAT I MEANT, JUST HEAR ME OUT.

MY RESEARCHERS TELL ME THAT IF WE FEED THAT INFANT CREATURE DOWN BELOW ON THIS JELLY--

IF IT MATURES TO QUEENHOOD SURROUNDED BY THE GOOP, IT WILL BECOME A QUEEN MOTHER ITSELF.

"YES, ULTIMATELY, MY GOAL IS TO MAKE MONEY,

"YOU CALL IT RUTHLESS,

"I CALL IT SURVIVAL,

"BUT THE TRUTH IS, ONCE I'VE GOT A SOURCE OF THIS JELLY CLOSE TO HOME--

"I'LL NEVER HAVE TO RISK ANOTHER LIFE TO GET IT,"

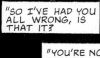

"SO I'VE HAD YOU ALL WRONG, IS THAT IT?

"YOU'RE NOT AN OPPORTUNIST AT ALL, YOU'RE THE BEST KIND OF HUMANITARIAN,"

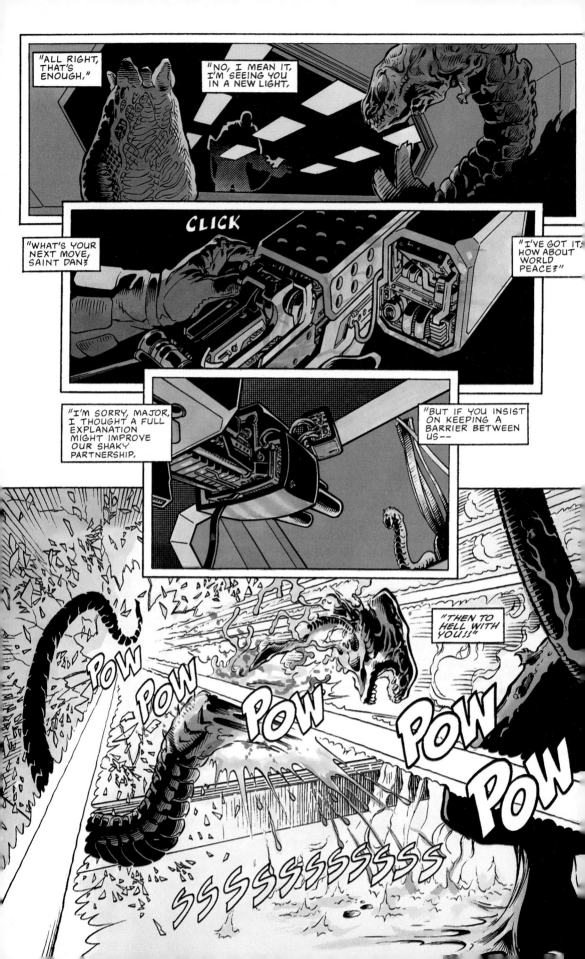

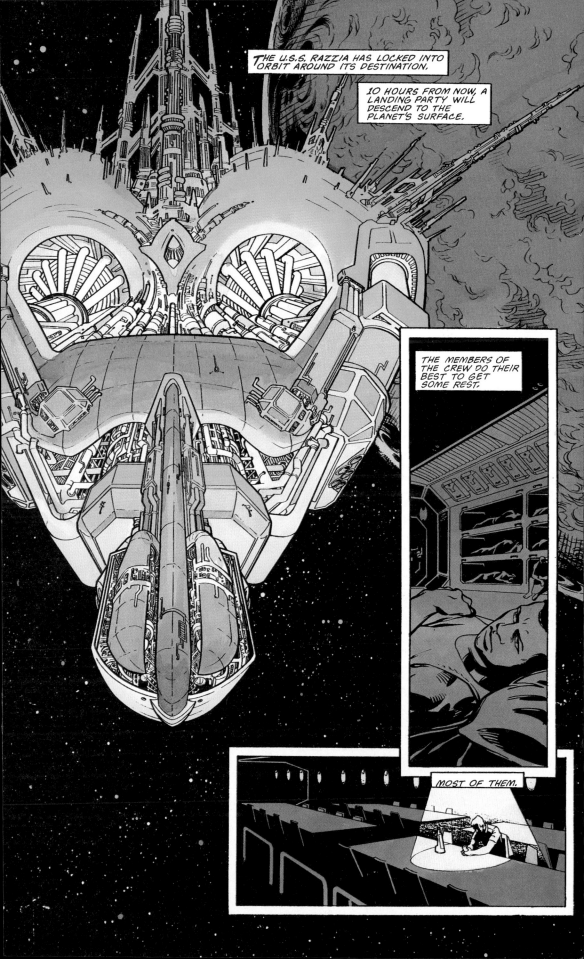

THE U.S.S. *RAZZIA* HAS LOCKED INTO ORBIT AROUND ITS DESTINATION.

10 HOURS FROM NOW, A LANDING PARTY WILL DESCEND TO THE PLANET'S SURFACE.

THE MEMBERS OF THE CREW DO THEIR BEST TO GET SOME REST.

MOST OF THEM.

MIND IF I JOIN YOU?

I WISH YOU WOULD.

I CAN'T BELIEVE I OVERLOOKED THIS POSSIBILITY. EVERYONE KNOWS THAT IF THIS MISSION FAILS, I'M HISTORY.

IF YOU ASK ME, IT'S BETTER THIS WAY.

SOMETHING TELLS ME YOU WOULD HAVE GOTTEN MORE THAN YOU BARGAINED FOR WITH DR. FRIEL AT THE HELM.

YOU'RE PROBABLY RIGHT, BUT THAT ISN'T THE POINT.

THIS SABOTAGE WILL CONTINUE, AND A LOT MORE THAN MONEY COULD BE LOST NEXT TIME.

IT'S HARD FOR ME TO BE SCARED OF A CORPORATE SPY WHEN I'VE BEEN FIGHTING MONSTERS FOR YEARS.

AND HOW OFTEN DID YOU RUN INTO INFILTRATION?

DON'T YOU SEE, YOU AND YOUR SOLDIERS HAVE ALWAYS BEEN UNITED AGAINST AN OBVIOUS THREAT.

TAKE IT FROM SOMEONE WHO KNOWS--

NOTHING IS DEADLIER THAN THE ENEMY WITHIN.

ZERO HOUR.

HEY, NICE CHOICE OF WEAPONS. MAYBE YOU CAN SCARE THE CRICKETS OFF WITH YOUR LOUSY PLAYING.

EAT IT, MILLHONE!

WHAT THE HELL'S UP HIS BUTT?

GRANT TOOK AWAY HIS XENO-ZIP, AND HE'S ON EDGE.

PLAYING MUSIC HELPS HIM RELAX, SO COOL IT, ALL RIGHT?

WAIT! WHAT ARE YOU DOING HERE?

YOUR NAME ISN'T ON THE LIST.

WELL, DR. FRIEL WAS SUPPOSED TO MAKE THE LANDING--

BUT HE'S IN NO CONDITION TO WORK RIGHT NOW.

DON'T WORRY, MR. GRANT, I KNOW JUST WHAT TO DO.

OKAY, PEOPLE, LET'S GET STRAPPED IN. WE'RE ABOUT TO DISENGAGE.

POWERFUL THRUSTERS ROAR IN SILENCE, RIPPING THE 70-TON LANDER FROM ITS MOORINGS.

BUT, AGAINST THE VAST BLACK VOID, IT'S A TINY VESSEL THAT GRACEFULLY STEALS AWAY FROM THE MOTHER SHIP.

INSIDE,

RRUUMMBBLLE

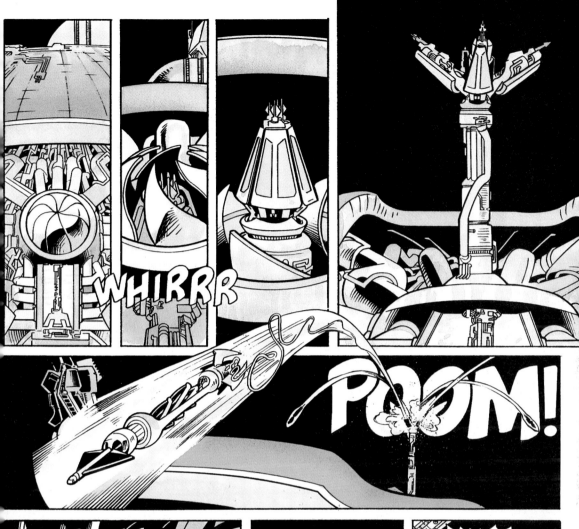

WHIRRR

POOM!

CHUNK!

CHUNK

CLINK

SPEED IT UP, O'CONNOR. THE ENEMY IS CLOSING IN.

OUTWALL ACTIVATION HAS BEEN INITIATED.

CLACK

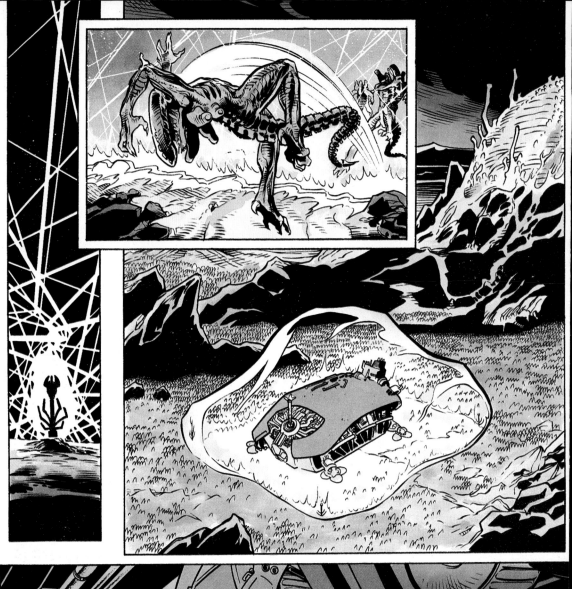

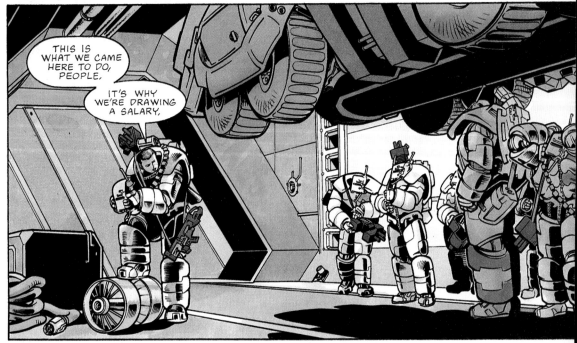

THIS IS WHAT WE CAME HERE TO DO, PEOPLE.

IT'S WHY WE'RE DRAWING A SALARY.

"HE'S A REGULAR ONE-MAN ARMY,"

SCRITCH

SCRITCH

MAJOR, WE GOT ONE ON THE SHIP,

HOLD ON, SOLDIER, SHOOT HIM WITH THAT, WE'LL HAVE BUG BLOOD ALL OVER THE HULL,

POOM

**ZZZZZZZTT!**

**WHUMP!**

IT AIN'T DEAD, IS IT?

DOUBT IT. THE ELECTRICAL CHARGE IN THE MESH IS PROBABLY JUST ENOUGH TO STUN IT.

**SSHHKON!**

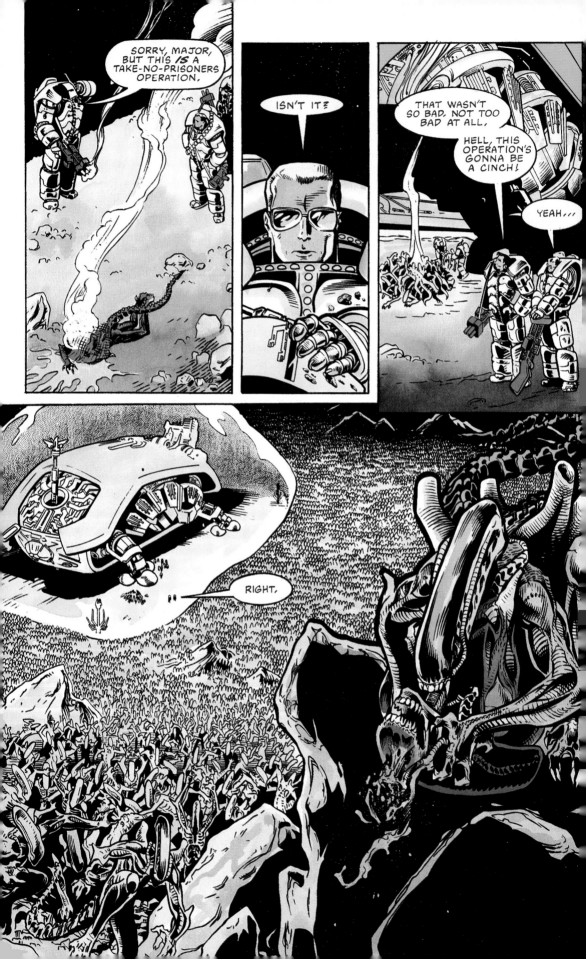

CLANG!

HEY, ELLIS, HOW 'BOUT A GAME?

WHAT?!

HOW THE HELL CAN YOU PLAY HORSESHOES WITH *THAT* JUST A FEW FEET AWAY?!

AHH, C'MON, YOU KNOW AS WELL AS I DO THEY CAN'T GET THROUGH THE OUTWALL.

MY ONLY COMPLAINT IS YOU CAN STILL SMELL 'EM.

MAKES IT PRETTY TOUGH TO EAT MY LUNCH.

NO, THEY CAN'T GET IN HERE, BUT PRETTY SOON, WE'RE GOING TO HAVE TO GO OUT *THERE!*

AND FROM THE LOOKS OF THINGS, I'D SAY THEY'RE READY FOR ONE HELL OF A FIGHT!

THAT'S ANOTHER THING, WHY ARE THEY BEATING ON *EACH OTHER?*

WHO CARES!

BACK ON EARTH, THEY'VE BEEN TRYING TO KILL US FOR MONTHS.

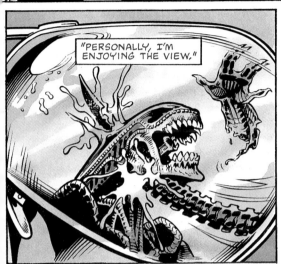

"PERSONALLY, I'M ENJOYING THE VIEW."

THAT CORPORAL HENRIKSEN IS ONE AMAZING SOLDIER.

I LIKE TO THINK ALL OF MY PEOPLE ARE, MR. GRANT.

I DIDN'T MEAN TO SLIGHT ANY OF YOUR TROOPS, MAJOR.

I JUST SINGLE HIM OUT BECAUSE OF WHAT I HEARD THE OTHER NIGHT.

HAH! YOU MEAN JASTROW'S COMMENTS ABOUT HIS BEING A SYNTH?

UH, NO, I MEANT WHAT HENRIKSEN SAID ABOUT BEING SENSITIVE TO THIS STUFF.

IT'S HARD TO IMAGINE HIM MORE FEROCIOUS THAN HE WAS THIS MORNING.

SO YOU DON'T THINK HENRIKSEN IS--

ISN'T THAT JASTROW'S XENO-ZIP?

HUH? OH YEAH, I MEANT TO GIVE IT BACK TO HIM.

"BUT JUDGING FROM HIS BEHAVIOR...."

OH, SHIT! CHECK IT OUT! HIS HEAD CAME RIGHT OFF!

"HE DOESN'T NEED ANY."

IT'S ALL RATHER PUZZLING.

PERHAPS THEY'RE EXECUTING SOME SORT OF POPULATION CONTROL, LIKE LEMMINGS MARCHING INTO THE SEA.

I'M GOING OUT TO STUDY THIS PHENOMENON MORE CLOSELY.

YOU'RE GONNA HAVE TO HOLD OFF ON THAT, DR. BEGALLI.

I JUST GOT THE WORD.

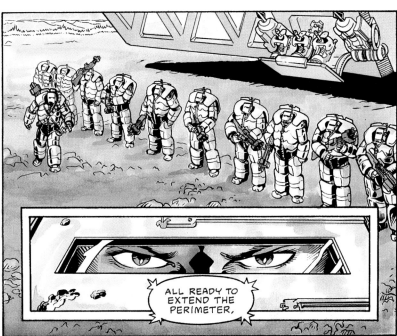

ALL READY TO EXTEND THE PERIMETER,

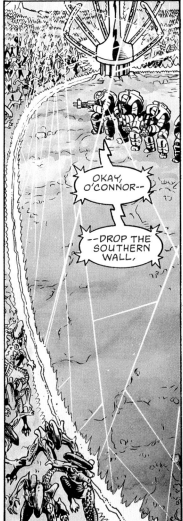

OKAY, O'CONNOR--

--DROP THE SOUTHERN WALL,

POOM POOM POOM

KA-BA-BOOM

WITHOUT A HITCH,

FOOP

JUST OVER THE CROWD--

--AND INTO THE--

--CLEAR?

SPLUTCH

SSSSS

SSSS

SSSS

DAMMIT, ARGENTO, YOU'RE GOING TO HAVE TO TRY IT AGAIN.

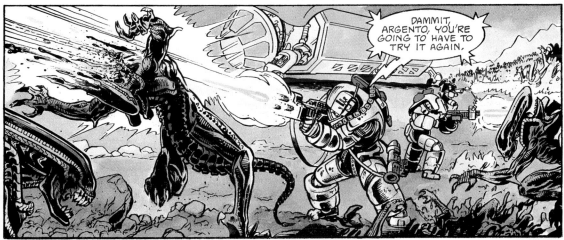

YOU GOT IT, MAJOR, BUT I THINK WE SHOULD TRY ANOTHER TACTIC, THIS IS TOUGHER THAN WE FIGURED.

IT'S LIKE TRYING TO EMPTY A RIVER WITH A BUCKET.

WE'RE NOT GOING TO GET THEM ALL THIS WAY.

FIRE, SMOKE, AND TORTURED SCREAMS FILL THE THIN ATMOSPHERE OF HELL.

FROM THE SAFETY OF THE LANDER, DANIEL GRANT WATCHES PEOPLE DIE, PEOPLE HE HAD TALKED TO AND EATEN WITH, AND COME TO RESPECT.

ALL DOOMED BY NEO-PHARM'S NEED FOR PROFIT.

HIS HEART FREEZES AS HE FEELS HIS SOUL SLIP INTO THE GRASP OF DEMONS.

SHHKOW!

SHHKOW!

YOU AIN'T GETTING ME, YOU #@%&ING #@%&S!

SHHKOW!!

ELLIS, MAN, I NEED SOME BACKUP!

SHHKOW!!

ELLIIISSS!!

SHHKOW!

ARGENTO, SCREW THE PERIMETER.

FIRE THE MORTARS INTO THEIR FRONT LINES.

FORGET ABOUT ARGENTO, MAJOR.

"HIS FIGHTING DAYS ARE OVER."

O'CONNOR, REACTIVATE THE SOUTHERN WALL, A.S.A.P!

WILL DO, MAJOR.

WAIT!

WAIT FOR WHAT, YOU MAGGOT?

FOR A FEW MORE OF THEM TO GET KILLED?

GO AHEAD, O'CONNOR, I'LL TAKE CARE OF THIS TURD.

NO, MR. GRANT. HE'S RIGHT.

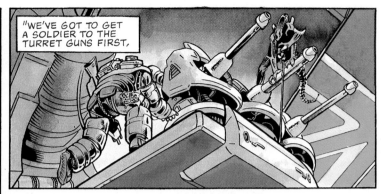

"WE'VE GOT TO GET A SOLDIER TO THE TURRET GUNS FIRST.

KABABOOM

"ONLY THEY CAN PROVIDE THE NECESSARY FIREPOWER TO DRIVE BACK THE BULK OF THE CREATURES."

IF I'D THROWN UP THE BARRIER, THE BLAST WOULD HAVE BEEN CONTAINED--

--RESULTING IN SEVERE DAMAGE TO THE LANDER.

THIS IS WHAT YOU MEANT, ISN'T IT, DR. BEGALLI?

UH.... OF COURSE!

WHAT ELSE?

IN A MATTER OF MINUTES, THE CREATURES ARE REPELLED, THE PERIMETER'S SOUTHERN WALL IS SECURED.

AND FIVE MARINES ARE DEAD.

JESUS....

THIS IS SOME BUSINESS YOU'RE IN, GRANT.

TELL ME, HOW DO YOU FIGURE THE DEATHS OF FIVE MARINES INTO YOUR OVER-HEAD?

MAJOR, PLEASE....

I....I.... JUST DIDN'T KNOW.

THAT MAKES TWO OF YOU, DOESN'T IT, DOCTOR?

DIDN'T YOU AND YOUR PALS SAY THESE CRICKETS WOULD BE HIBERNATING?

WELL, I'M AS SURPRISED AS YOU ARE, MAJOR.

I'LL SEE WHAT I CAN MAKE OF ALL THIS, IF YOU'LL EXCUSE ME.

MAJOR, HAVE YOU SEEN JASTROW?

I JUST HEARD HIM SHOUTING A FEW MINUTES AGO, BUT I CAN'T FIND HIM NOW.

UHH--

I'M.... SORRY, ELLIS.

THERE WAS NOTHING ANYBODY COULD DO.

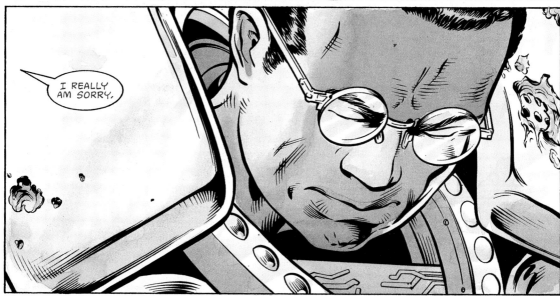

I REALLY AM SORRY.

I DON'T KNOW WHAT TO SAY.

MAYBE YOU WANT TO QUIT--

WRONG! MARINES DON'T QUIT, MISTER.

MY COUNTRY SENT ME HERE TO GET SOMETHING, AND I'VE LOST TOO MANY PEOPLE TO GO HOME EMPTY-HANDED NOW.

I JUST WANTED YOU TO KNOW THAT I DON'T LIKE IT.

UH, PARDON ME, MAJOR, MR. GRANT, BUT I THINK I HAVE SOME GOOD NEWS.

I BELIEVE WHAT WE ARE WITNESSING IS AN INTERSPECIES WAR.

I CAN ONLY GUESS HOW IT HAPPENED, BUT IT APPEARS THE RED CREATURES ARE MUTATIONS, A SEPARATE SPECIES FROM THE MORE FAMILIAR BLACK CREATURES.

THUS, IT WOULD APPEAR THEY ARE FIGHTING FOR TERRITORIAL CONTROL.

YOU MEAN LIKE ANTS?!

PRECISELY.

SO WHY IS THAT GOOD NEWS?

WELL, IF WE COULD SWAY THE BATTLE IN FAVOR OF ONE SIDE, THERE WOULD VERY LIKELY BE A ROUT,

LEAVING THIS HIVE RELATIVELY CLEAR AND UNPROTECTED.

BUT THAT TURRET CARRIES OUR BEST FIREPOWER, AND IT DIDN'T DO A THING.

HOW CAN WE SWAY THE BATTLE?

EASY, MR. GRANT.

WE NUKE 'EM!

WELL?

A TACTICAL NUCLEAR STRIKE ON THE MUTANTS' HIVE WOULD PROVE MOST EFFECTIVE.

OF COURSE, WE WOULD HAVE TO LOCATE THE NEW HIVE FIRST.

THAT SHOULDN'T BE A PROBLEM. I'LL BUZZ THE ORBITER TO GET ON IT RIGHT AWAY.

GOOD. THE SOONER WE GO IN, THE SOONER WE CAN END THIS.

"WE"? YOU AREN'T GOING ANYWHERE, GRANT.

THAT'S WHERE YOU'RE WRONG, MAJOR. I AM GOING INTO THAT HIVE WITH YOU.

I DON'T WANT ANY CIVILIANS--

SAVE IT, MAJOR!

ON A PRACTICAL LEVEL, YOU NEED MANPOWER BADLY.

AND ON A MORAL LEVEL, I NEED TO DO THIS.

CAN YOU UNDERSTAND THAT, MAJOR? IF I'M EVER TO LOOK MYSELF IN THE MIRROR AGAIN, I NEED TO DO THIS.

GRANT'S LOGIC IS UNASSAILABLE.

BUT MORE IMPORTANTLY, SO IS HIS SINCERITY.

THEN YOU'D BETTER SUIT UP PRONTO. YOU'LL FIND THE ARMOR JUST BEHIND THE CARGO DRONE.

IT IS ONLY THROUGH THIS BAPTISM OF FIRE THAT HE FEELS HE CAN FIND REDEMPTION.

PROVIDED HE DOESN'T DIE FIRST.

SICK WITH SHAME AND MORE THAN A LITTLE AFRAID, THE LAST THING ON HIS MIND IS--

vvvip

--SABOTAGE.

JUST GREAT!

CAN'T WORRY ABOUT IT NOW, MUST BE ANOTHER SUIT OF ARMOR IN HERE SOMEWHERE.

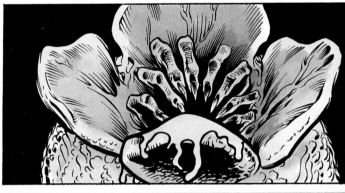

SCR-EEE

DANIEL GRANT IS WELL ACQUAINTED WITH ALIEN LARVAE. HE'S SEEN HUNDREDS OF THEM INFECT TEST ANIMALS IN HIS RESEARCH LABS.

INCLUDING ONE LION.

OF COURSE, ALL THOSE ANIMALS WERE CAGED.

THEY COULD NEVER SIMPLY RUN AWAY.

NOT THAT IT WOULD HAVE DONE THEM ANY GOOD.

HAAALP!!

WHACK

SHHH KOW!!

WHOA! YOU SURE SAVED MY ASS, SOLDIER!

YEAH, WELL, THAT'S MY JOB.

LOOKS LIKE ONE OF YOUR PETS WANDERED OFF THE BEATEN TRACK.

SSSSSSS

NO WAY, MAJOR! I ONLY AUTHORIZED *ONE* CREATURE FOR INCUBATION. THIS WAS A BLATANT ATTEMPT ON MY LIFE.

TAKE A LOOK IN THE ARMORY CLOSET!

I WAS THE ONLY ONE NOT ARMORED, SO IT'S OBVIOUS THIS THING WAS PLANTED TO GET ME WHEN I CAME BACK HERE.

IT'S GOT TO BE BEGALLI. HE MUST STILL BE WORKING FOR THOSE SCUMBAGS AT MEDTECH. I WANT YOU TO PUT THAT BASTARD UNDER ARREST--

--OR HANG HIM.

REIN YOURSELF IN, GRANT.

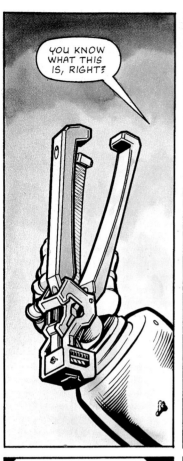

YOU KNOW WHAT THIS IS, RIGHT?

OF COURSE, IT'S A TIMER CLAMP.

IT'S USED TO HOLD THE LIPS OF AN EGG SHUT TO INSURE THE CREATURE CAN'T ESCAPE DURING TRANSPORTATION.

AND IT AUTOMATICALLY FALLS OFF WHEN THE TIMER EXPIRES. NOBODY IS ANY-WHERE NEAR THE EGG WHEN IT "ACTIVATES."

SO?

SO, ANYONE COULD HAVE PLANTED THIS EGG... EVEN ME.

BEGALLI IS THE ONLY ALIEN EXPERT IN THE LANDING PARTY.

MAYBE YOU DON'T KNOW THIS, BUT ALL RADIO SIGNALS ARE SCRAMBLED BY THOSE HIVES. ONCE INSIDE, WE'LL HAVE NO COM-MUNICATION WITH THE LANDER.

WE'RE GOING TO NEED "THAT BASTARD" IN THERE MORE THAN ANY OTHER CREW MEMBER.

WITHOUT HIM, THIS OPERATION IS DEAD IN THE WATER.

YOU STILL WANT ME TO BUST HIM?

NO, I GUESS NOT.

I'M GOING TO START THE SEARCH AND DESTROY MISSION ON THE RIVAL HIVE.

TRY TO STAY OUT OF TROUBLE, OKAY?

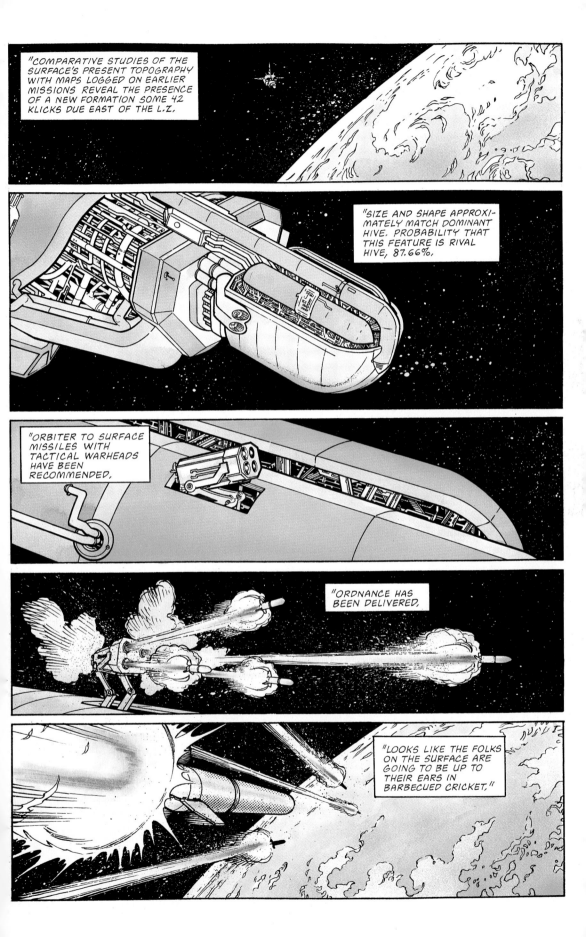

THE MOTHER OF A NATION HAS TIME FOR ONLY ONE SCREAM OF ANGUISH.

A SCREAM HEARD BY EACH OF HER VAST BROOD.

A SCREAM WHICH SOUNDS THE DEATH KNELL OF THE NEW ORDER.

IT WORKED!

THE REDS ARE RETREATING TO THE OTHER HIVE.

THIS ONE SHOULD BE CLEAR IN A FEW MINUTES.

THEN LET'S GET MOVING! WHO'S GOING IN?

EVERYONE BUT THE TECHNICAL CREW --AND ELLIS.

MAKES SENSE, HE'S TAKING JASTROW'S DEATH PRETTY HARD.

THEY GREW UP TOGETHER, JOINED THE CORPS TOGETHER, AND FOUGHT FOR YEARS IN THE SAME UNIT.

HE'S A GOOD MARINE, AND HE'LL BE OKAY IN A FEW DAYS, BUT I'D RATHER NOT HAVE HIM IN CLOSE COMBAT RIGHT NOW.

BESIDES, SOMEONE HAS TO MAN THE GUNS.

ALL SET, MAJOR.

HOW ABOUT YOU, GRANT? YOU GONNA BE OKAY?

DON'T WORRY ABOUT ME, MAJOR. I CAN TAKE CARE OF MYSELF!

ALL RIGHT, THEN.

O'CONNOR, DROP THE SOUTHERN BORDER.

POOM!

THIS SORT OF FIGHT IS WHAT THE MARINES EXPECTED ON THE ALIEN HOMEWORLD, WHAT THEY'RE USED TO.

IT IS NOT A BATTLE THEY EXECUTE, BUT A SWIFT AND BRUTAL VENGEANCE FOR THEIR COMRADES LOST.

WELL, MAJOR, WERE MY COMBAT SKILLS SATISFACTORY?

PAT YOURSELF ON THE BACK LATER, GRANT, AND PUT YOUR DAMN HELMET BACK ON!

O'CONNOR, DROP THE NEW SOUTHERN BORDER, AND SEND IN THE CARGO DRONE.

THIS IS THE LAST RADIO CONTACT TILL WE GET BACK OUT. OVER AND OUT.

OKAY, DR. BEGALLI, GET YOUR BUTT UP FRONT.

WELL, DOCTOR, WHICH WAY TO THE "BURIED TREASURE"?

WELL, THE PHEROMONE READINGS SEEM TO JIBE WITH WHAT I EXPECTED.

LET'S TRY *THIS* WAY.

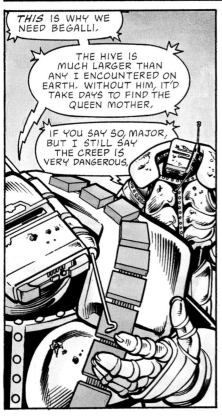

*THIS* IS WHY WE NEED BEGALLI.

THE HIVE IS MUCH LARGER THAN ANY I ENCOUNTERED ON EARTH. WITHOUT HIM, IT'D TAKE DAYS TO FIND THE QUEEN MOTHER.

IF YOU SAY SO, MAJOR, BUT I STILL SAY THE CREEP IS VERY DANGEROUS.

YAAAAA

THE QUEEN MOTHER'S ELITE GUARD,

PSYCHICALLY LINKED TO THE MATRIARCH, THEY ARE RELEASED ONLY WHEN SHE SENSES EXTREME DANGER,

THE MARINES WERE WARNED ABOUT THESE ESPECIALLY VICIOUS CREATURES,

NO TEAM OF SOLDIERS COULD BE BETTER PREPARED, OR BETTER EQUIPPED, TO BATTLE THE "SUPER ALIENS,"

THE REWARD FOR THEIR PREPARATION IS A VICTORY,,,

...OF SORTS.

IS....IS EVERYONE ALL RIGHT?

COME ON, YOU LITTLE BASTARD,

YOU'RE TAKING US TO THE QUEEN MOTHER'S CHAMBERS, OR I'LL BLOW YOUR HEAD OFF.

THERE ARE MORE SURPRISES HERE THAN I FIGURED ON, SO I WANT YOU THREE TO WATCH OUR BACKS.

THE RADIOS DON'T FUNCTION LONG DISTANCE IN THE HIVES, SO IF WE DON'T RETURN IN TWO HOURS, GET BACK TO THE LANDER, AND GET OUT OF HERE.

MAJOR, DO YOU REALLY THINK IT'S WORTH ALL THIS TROUBLE, I MEAN, THIS JELLY WE'RE AFTER?

AH-AH-AH, HENRIKSEN, DON'T START THINKING NOW.

IT'LL ONLY DISTRACT YOU.

LOOK! LOOK AT IT ALL!

I NEVER THOUGHT I'D SEE THIS MUCH UP CLOSE.

GOD, IT'S BEAUTIFUL.

BEAUTIFUL?! EIGHT GOOD PEOPLE DIED FOR THAT CRAP! DOESN'T THAT MEAN ANYTHING TO YOU?

BUT, MR. GRANT, SIR, THIS EXPEDITION WAS YOUR IDEA.

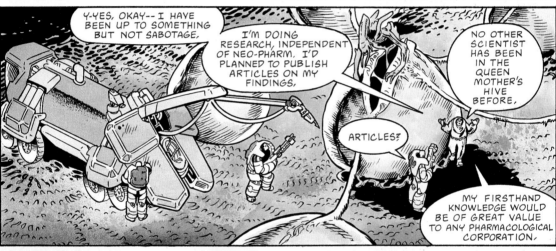

AIIII!!!SPLUTCH!

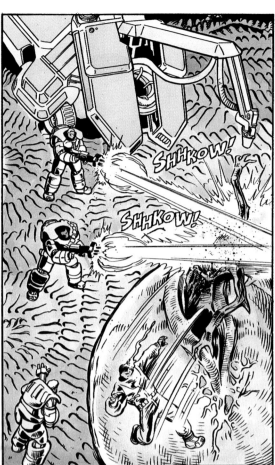

SHHKOW!

SHHKOW!

I DON'T GET IT.

ONLY A FEW PEOPLE EVEN KNEW ABOUT THE ALIEN INCUBATION PROJECT.

IF HE DIDN'T SABOTAGE IT, WHO DID?

ALL RIGHT, GRANT, MAJOR LEE, DROP YOUR WEAPONS.

IT'S KIND OF FUNNY, ISN'T IT, GRANT? YOU'VE COME SO FAR. I MEAN, YOU'VE ACTUALLY ATTAINED YOUR GOAL.

BUT JUST ONE BLAST FROM THIS GUN, AND NEO-PHARM, THE XENO-ZIP PATENT, AND ALL OF GRANT ENTERPRISES WILL BE UP FOR GRABS.

BEST OF ALL, NO WITNESSES, OTHER THAN THE MAJOR HERE, AND I'LL BET SHE'S DYING TO PULL THE TRIGGER HERSELF.

I DON'T GET IT, YOU RISKED YOUR LIFE WITH THE REST OF US.

LIFE HAS NO MEANING TO HIM, MAJOR. HE'S AN ANDROID, BUILT AND PROGRAMMED BY MEDTECH TO RUIN ME.

RIGHT, "HENRIKSEN"?

HEH, SURE, THAT'S IT. HEH HEH

HA HA HA HA HA

LAUGH WHILE YOU CAN, CORPORAL.

SHHKOW!

DAMMIT, MAJOR, I THOUGHT YOU SAW THINGS MY WAY.

AND I REALLY LIKED YOU, TOO.

SMAAK!

OH, THAT WAS A MISTAKE, GRANT.

YOU THINK YOU'RE TOUGH, TRAINING IN A GYM WITH A TEACHER,

BUT INSIDE, ALL YOU RICH MAGGOTS ARE SOFT AS--

THOK!

OOOF!

WHUUMP!

I WAS WRONG, YOU'RE TOO DAMN ARROGANT TO BE AN ANDROID.

OOOH, I THINK MY HIP IS BROKEN.

BUT... SHOULDN'T I BE DEAD?

THE UNDER-PLATING ON THIS ARMOR IS DESIGNED TO WITHSTAND SEVERE CONCUSSIONS.

STILL, YOU'RE PROBABLY RIGHT ABOUT THAT HIP, YOU'RE GO-ING TO NEED SOME HELP.

SOON.

SPIES, RENEGADES, AND HIT MEN. I THINK IT'S TIME I DROPPED OUT OF THE CORPORATE WORLD.

BUT NOT BEFORE WE TAKE THIS LOAD HOME, RIGHT?

YOU SAID IT YOURSELF THIS MORNING, MAJOR. TOO MANY HAVE DIED FOR US TO LEAVE IT ALL BEHIND NOW.

YEAH, WHATEVER.

I GUESS THIS MAKES YOU FEEL PRETTY GOOD-- BEING THE HERO, SAVING MY LIFE.

JUST RETURNING THE FAVOR, MAJOR.

PLEASE ACTIVATE THE DRONE, MAJOR, IT'S SET TO FOLLOW US. WHEN WE HIT OPEN AIR, IT'LL HOME IN ON THE LANDER.

HENRIKSEN, YOU LEAD THE WAY.

I STILL THINK YOU SHOULD BE WEARING MORE ARMOR, AND WHAT ABOUT OUR HELMETS?

FORGET THE HELMETS, WE'VE GOT ENOUGH WEIGHT TO SLOW US DOWN AS IT IS.

BESIDES, THE CREATURES ARE MILES FROM HERE.

BA-BOOM!!

O'CONNOR, DROP ALL WALLS OF THE PERIMETER AND TELL CAPTAIN NASH TO START THE ENGINES!

PREPARE FOR AN IMMEDIATE EMERGENCY LIFTOFF!

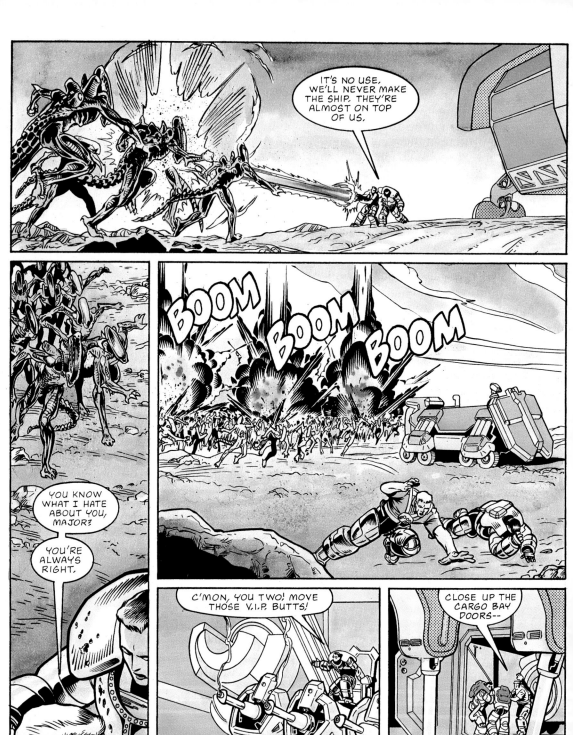

IT'S NO USE, WE'LL NEVER MAKE THE SHIP. THEY'RE ALMOST ON TOP OF US.

BOOM BOOM! BOOM

YOU KNOW WHAT I HATE ABOUT YOU, MAJOR?

YOU'RE ALWAYS RIGHT.

C'MON, YOU TWO! MOVE THOSE V.I.P. BUTTS!

CLOSE UP THE CARGO BAY DOORS--

WE'RE WAY AHEAD OF YOU, MR. GRANT.

BACK ON THE MOTHER SHIP:

SO YOU'LL BE OKAY?

YEAH, JUST A HAIRLINE FRACTURE, FIVE WEEKS IN THE SLEEPER TUBE AND I CAN START PHYSICAL THERAPY ON EARTH.

I GUESS YOU'RE DOING PRETTY WELL YOURSELF.

BETTER THAN I'VE A RIGHT TO, MAJOR.

IF I COULD DO THE WHOLE THING OVER AGAIN, I WOULDN'T DO IT AT ALL, NOT AT THE COST OF ELEVEN GOOD KIDS.

OH, YEAH, I FORGOT, YOU'RE A "CHANGED MAN."

YOU'RE VERY HARD TO WIN OVER, MAJOR LEE, WHICH IS WHY I'M GLAD YOU'RE ON MY SIDE.

IT'S BEEN A LONG HARD, HORRIBLE DAY, BUT I FEEL I'VE COME AWAY FROM ALL THIS A WISER, BETTER...PERSON.

SEE? YOU REALLY CAN LEARN SOMETHING NEW EVERY DAY.

"GOOD NIGHT, MAJOR."

# Biographies

Mike Richardson, founder and publisher of Dark Horse Comics, is one of the bona-fide movers and shakers in the industry, a seemingly inexhaustible fountain of ideas and stories, and a genuinely nice guy. However, he is not above using his nice-guy image and his big-kid looks to lure people into thinking that he just fell off the turnip truck. Watch yourself around him.

John Arcudi was born at an early age and hasn't gotten any younger since. He was raised by two older brothers, but they put him back down when their father caught them. John has had to deal with hard times and loss, but when "She's the Sheriff" was canceled, that was the last straw. These days, John is a shell of his former self, but he's quick to add that if you run into his former self, tell him that his shell misses him.

Damon Willis has spent the ten years since he graduated from the University of Maryland accumulating old comics, books, and magazines. He has pencilled, colored, inked, lettered, and scripted for a variety of companies and is currently working on *Doctor Cyborg* for Attention! Publishing and *The Body* for Penthouse Comix. Damon lives in Rockville, Maryland with a couple of temperamental computers.

Karl's Story: Scores would be settled before the slow boat to Long Beach pulled out of the harbor. The air was thick, and hot lead vied for maximum occupancy. The Tall Man stepped over his latest masterpiece and croaked to the penciller with the sucking chest wound, "Punk. the secret to good inking is laying down a thin film of noir." The Tall Man gave the little penciller his last bullet. He never saw so much lead.

Arthur Suydam has enjoyed a successful career as a comic-book artist, children's book illustrator, cover artist, and color designer. Long considered one of the premier stylists in the field, Suydam has won acclaim for his painted covers for various Dark Horse Aliens books. His oversized art book, *Visions: The Art of Arthur Suydam*, was published by Dark Horse in 1995. Also a talented musician, Suydam resides in New York City.

John Bolton paints in an eerie, prop-filled studio in North London. An award-winning artist who has worked on books with Chris Claremont, Neil Gaiman, Clive Barker, Sam Raimi, Anne Rice, and many others, and whose ethereal vampire-women and magical creatures have made his work much sought after, John has handled assignments for every major publisher in the comics field.

# ALIENS™
## GENOCIDE
### GALLERY

The following paintings, by award-winning illustrator Arthur Suydam, were done for the *Alien³* and *Aliens: Genocide* comic-book series.

Suydam © 91

## ALIENS

**FEMALE WAR**
(formerly *Aliens: Earth War*)
Verheiden • Kieth
112-page color paperback
ISBN: 1-85286-784-1 £11.99

**HIVE**
Prosser • Jones
112-page color paperback
ISBN: 1-85286-469-9 £8.99

**LABYRINTH**
Woodring • Plunkett
136-page color paperback
ISBN: 1-85286-668-3 £9.99

**NIGHTMARE ASYLUM**
(formerly *Aliens: Book Two*)
Verheiden • Beauvais
112-page color paperback
ISBN: 1-85286-765-5 £11.99

**NEWT'S TALE**
Richardson • Somerville • Garvey
96-page color paperback
ISBN: 1-85286-575-x £6.99

**ROGUE**
Edginton • Simpson
112-page color paperback
ISBN: 1-85286-592-x £8.99

**OUTBREAK**
(formerly *Aliens: Book One*)
Verheiden • Nelson
168-page B&W paperback
ISBN: 1-85286-756-6 £11.99

**STRONGHOLD**
Arcudi • Mahnke • Palmiotti
112-page color paperback
ISBN: 1-85286-733-7 £9.99

## ALIENS VS PREDATOR

**ALIENS VS PREDATOR**
Stradley • Warner
176-page color paperback
ISBN: 1-85286-413-3 £10.99

**ALIENS VS PREDATOR: WAR**
Stradley • Warner
200-page color paperback
ISBN: 1-85286-703-5 £12.99

## PREDATOR

**PREDATOR**
Verheiden • Warner • Randall
168-page color paperback
ISBN: 1-85286-377-3 £7.50

**PREDATOR: BIG GAME**
Arcudi • Dorkin • Gil
112-page color paperback
ISBN: 1-85286-454-0 £7.50

**PREDATOR: COLD WAR**
Verheiden • Randall • Mitchell
112-page color paperback
ISBN: 1-85286-576-8 £8.99

All *Aliens* and *Predator* publications are available through most
good bookshops or direct from our mail order service at Titan Books.
For a free graphic novels catalogue or to order, telephone
01536 763 631 with your credit card details or contact Titan Books
Mail Order, PO Box 54, Desborough, Northants, NN14 2UH,
quoting reference AGEN/GN.